Write It Out

Copyright © 2017 by Jordan Corcoran

ISBN-10: 1-944134-10-7
ISBN-13: 978-1-944134-10-5

Printed in the United States of America.

WRITE it OUT

Listen, LUCY.
EXPRESS YOURSELF, CREATIVELY

WRITTEN BY:
JORDAN CORCORAN

illustrated by: Erin Fox

To my parents:

I know I haven't shut up in 30 years, so I hope you don't regret teaching me to speak my mind. You always pushed me to use my voice. At times, I'm sure it had to be funny, cringe-worthy, annoying and all around heartbreaking to hear what I had to say, but my voice has made me into the person that I am. Thank you for making sure I was heard.

I love you.

{ Listen, LUCY. }

EXPRESS YOURSELF, CREATIVELY.

About Listen Lucy:

ListenLucy.org is a place to express yourself. Freely. Creatively. Anonymously. A place to find comfort in seeing that you are not alone.

After being diagnosed with Generalized Anxiety Disorder and Panic Disorder when I was a freshman in college, writing became such an important outlet for me. Because it was so cathartic for me, I wanted to create a safe, judgement-free place for people to write about and share their lives. It has become such a beautiful light in a somewhat dark world.

Over the past 4 years, I have spoken to thousands of people in middle school, high school and college as well as professionals in the mental health field. I have shared my story and my mission and have been able to see how important and necessary this outlet and this conversation is.

The words of ListenLucy.org have moved me. They are truthful, unfiltered and incredibly beautiful. I want to share some with you. In between each writing prompt in this journal is a quote from one of the anonymous writers from our website. When you read them, I hope these words speak to you as they did to me. Keep them with you always.

I hope something that you read or write about in this journal lights a spark in you. If so, feel free to tell us about it at ListenLucy.org.

{Welcome}

In my darkest hours of battling my anxiety disorder, I am trapped in my head with no way to escape. My thoughts are so manic and moving so fast that I can't complete a single thought. My brain makes me feel like a prisoner in my own body. It runs wild and I am reduced to tears–usually on the floor in my bathroom–as I fight off a panic attack. It's a nightmare. Fighting your own mind is unbelievably exhausting and extremely isolating. It freaking sucks. It feels like I can't shut my brain off and it's what I am so desperate to do. I feel hopeless.

Through all of that chaos, writing is what calms my mind. It relaxes those thoughts. It soothes my soul.

When my mind is calm and I take a minute to myself, I write out how I am feeling. I write about what is destroying me. I write about the things in my life that I am so grateful for that I could cry. I write about loss and love. Failures and dreams. I write how I am feeling without worrying about judgement or ridicule. I write and then I am healed. It is cathartic and super amazing and I want to share that with you.

Take this book. Use it as a journal. Throw it in your bag and keep it with you. Write it out. Be brutally honest. Use it as your escape route from your own mind.

Let yourself heal. Be free.

Jordan
Founder, ListenLucy.org

the more

POSITIVE
ENERGY

you put into the world,
the more that will come
back to you. And that's
what I plan to do.

{ }

Life can be hard and
confusing and difficult.
It can also be rewarding and
beautiful
Sometimes we forget to focus on
the good things we experience
every day. At the bare minimum,
every day we have the ability to

love, to laugh and to be kind.

What is your favorite thing about your life?

_____

_____

_____

_____

IN TODAY'S
WORLD
ACCEPTANCE
SEEMS DIFFICULT
TO FIND
{ }

You would think in present day, that acceptance is something that would be easily found. But it isn't. We see awful things on the news, social media and in our everyday lives. As if it that isn't enough, we talk down to ourselves and judge ourselves. We always think we could be better; that we could be more.

Why is it so difficult?

What could you do to accept yourself more today?

you have to remember to LOVE yourself first.

{ }

Whenever I struggle, slip up or fail, I take it so hard. I look in the mirror and talk down to myself. I feel failure pumping in my veins and I can't look myself in my eye. I repeat over and over again,
"Why am I like this? Why am I wired like this?"

Why do you think it is so hard to accept yourself?

I WANT PEOPLE TO
LIKE ME
or at least acknowledge
MY EXISTANCE
I FEEL LIKE I SHOULD
TRY HARDER TO FEEL.

{ }

Write out all of the mean, hurtful things you say about yourself. Then color in the page until you can no longer read the words. Get those words out of you and leave them out.

THE LIGHT
is getting
BRIGHTER
but yet it's so
FAR AWAY.

{ }

Sometimes, the enormity of what I want to accomplish leaves me feeling stuck. I have so much to do in order to change the world and I am determined to make that happen. I make a list of what I can do to accomplish something that day and tell myself that little by little, a little becomes a lot.

What are you going to do today to get yourself closer to reaching your goal?

TELL YOURSELF HOWCOOL YOU ARE every single day.

{ }

Write 5 *positive* things in your life and
5 *positive* things you want for your life.

Let these things become your motivation.

{1}_____   {1}_____

{2}_____   {2}_____

{3}_____   {3}_____

{4}_____   {4}_____

{5}_____   {5}_____

WE ALL STRUGGLE.
WE ALL HAVE THINGS
THAT STOP US IN OUR
TRACKS AND WE SAY
SMALL, QUIET PRAYERS
TO TRY AND WILL A CHANGE
IN OUR SITUATION.

{ }

My anxiety is something that I struggle with daily. Sometimes I hate who I am. I am working on that.

What is your battle? What are you working on accepting about yourself?

_____

_____

_____

_____

23

I'VE GOT TO KNOW *in advance* WHEN I AM *vulnerable* AND BE ABLE TO CONTROL MY *emotions.*

{ }

One night, I was driving to a Listen, Lucy event at The University of Pittsburgh. On the highway, a really rude guy cut me off and slammed on his breaks while doing it–almost causing me to crash into him–and then had the audacity to give me the finger. I couldn't believe it. Fury took over me. I sped up. I beeped. I yelled horrible things. I made sure he saw my middle finger, and then I went to talk to young people about kindness and acceptance. Isn't that ironic? Don't ya think? Anger does not look good on me...or on anyone really.

What do you get angry about often? How you can you fix it for tomorrow?

SEE, HALF OF THE PROBLEM WAS, AND IS, I've been blind TO MY OWN Problems

{ }

My mental illness, at its worst, makes me *feel* isolated, alone and really misunderstood. It sucks. I wouldn't wish it upon anyone.

What do you think others don't understand about you? How does that make you feel?

_____

_____

_____

_____

_____

_____

·THIS · IS · FOR · YOU·

Guys & Girls

MY FAMILY; MY FRIENDS;
MY ROCKS; MY ENTIRE WORLD.

{ }

Support is so important. I could never justly express how much the people in my life mean to me. I have tried but have always failed. I can only hope they know how much I love them, how much they impact my life and how I could never be who I am today without them in my life.

Who is your support system?
What do you want them to know?
Pour your heart out on this page.

_____

_____

_____

_____

ONE OF THE
THINGS

I LOVE
ABOUT
MYSELF

IS MY
PAST.

{ }

Write a letter to your younger self.

What do you wish you knew back then?

(FYI I could fill up this entire book with things I wish I knew then...most of it would read "LET. IT. GO.")

Dear

_____

_____

_____

_____

_____

Love,

I LEARNED THAT I HAVE AN

obligation

=TO =FIGHT= FOR= MY=

HEALTH

AND MY

Confidence

{ }

After I have a bad run with my mental illness, I need to let myself feel sad and to wallow for a bit. I don't plan it, but it does help me heal. I get on my couch, nap and turn off all of my electronic devices. I get off the grid until I am ready to take the world on again.

What do you do to get off the grid? Why does this help you?

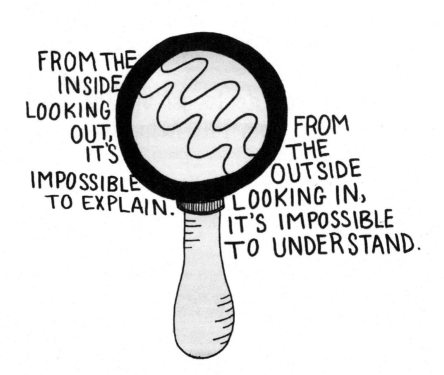

FROM THE
INSIDE
LOOKING
OUT,
IT'S
IMPOSSIBLE
TO EXPLAIN.

FROM
THE
OUTSIDE
LOOKING IN,
IT'S IMPOSSIBLE
TO UNDERSTAND.

{ }

We have all been betrayed in our lives.
We have all had people who turned out to be
different than we expected.

How did that make you feel?

_____

_____

_____

_____

_____

_____

_____

_____

_____

I feel empty.
The kind of empty
where a cold shower
washes over me but
I don't feel the
drops of
water hit my skin.

{ }

How are you today?
(Don't say fine or good. Tell the truth.)

_____

_____

_____

_____

_____

_____

_____

_____

I NEVER THOUGHT
THAT I WOULD
HAVE THE COURAGE
TO WRITE ABOUT
[MY STRUGGLE]
BUT I WOKE UP
TODAY FEELING
VERY
Thankful
AND
Motivated.

{ }

My husband. Beyoncé. Doritos. My incredible family. Good books. Sunshine. The Internet. Memes. Smartphones. My hilarious friends. Nori's Black Book. Land'O'Lakes American cheese. My trip abroad to London. My health. My humor. My freedom to be who I want to be. Tom Segura. Computers. Netflix. Rap Music. Andra Day. YouTube. My own struggle. Reality TV. Journals. Pizza. Hannibal Buress. Kindness. Group Chats. Broadway. School supplies. Graphic Tees. Being able to use "Do Not Disturb" on group chats. Diet Pepsi. Barack Obama and Joe Biden's bromance. Bad ass women. The Listen, Lucy Community. GPS. The Office. Dorinda Medley. Social Media. My ambition. Cozy sweatshirts. My home. Naps. My kind heart.

What are you grateful for?

YOU ARE GOING TO FAIL,

You Should!

DON'T LET IT DETER YOU
FROM YOUR DREAMS OR
SHAKE YOUR CONFIDENCE
RATHER LET IT MOTIVATE
YOU AND LEARN FROM IT.

{ }

Listen, Lucy is my dream. It's my *passion*. I believe in it more than I believe in most things. It is worth my time and energy; my tears and frustration. It is worth the sleepless nights and the failures; both tiny and huge.
It is worth it because it is my *dream*.

What is your dream? Why is it worth it?

You will also have your moment when you can look back on a crappy time in your life and see how far you have come and think "I am awesome."

{ }

What super crappy or not-so-great moment worked out OK?

(Remember this the next time something crappy happens.)

_____

_____

_____

_____

_____

_____

_____

_____

I HAVE SO MANY
THINGS TO BE
PROUD
of, and one day
I WILL SEE THAT.
Because of You,
people like me
recognize it's just
A BAD DAY
not a bad life.

{ }

What is something you accomplished that you didn't think you could accomplish?

(It can be something small or something huge. Accomplished is accomplished.)

THE AWESOME THING ABOUT BEING

·O· ·P· ·E· ·N·

ABOUT YOUR STRUGGLES IS THAT
THERE ARE TIMES WHEN THINGS
come full circle
YOU REMEMBER TALKING ABOUT
HOW BAD IT WAS AT A CERTAIN
POINT IN YOUR LIFE AND YOU
REALIZE THAT MAY BE THE
TIME YOU GOT A GRIP ON
your situation.

{ }

When I am in the eye of the storm of a panic attack, I can't see what I am doing or how I am acting. I am really in my own version of *survival* mode. There was a time not so long ago that I was in a bush outside of Nordstrom praying for some sort of divine intervention to stop the panic in my body. For real. I am not making that up. I, a grown woman, was in a bush trying anything I could to survive that moment. But, when the storm passes and I look back at what was happening during the attack, it feels like I was a completely different person. It shocks me.

Have you ever felt that way? What would you want to tell that version of yourself?

(For example: "Jordan. Take your medication and maybe get out of the bush.")

_____

_____

_____

_____

_____

SOMETIMES LIFE DEALS YOU AN UNFORTUNATE SET,

A SHORT HAND.

A DECK OF 51 CARDS

INSTEAD OF 52,

a card missing that may be the one that completes a full house, one that you wish you have until this very day.

{ }

Hours before my grandpa passed away, I went to visit him. I was the only family member there for a brief time and had a minute to sit with him and hold his hand. He wasn't awake, but I remember thinking, "Come on. Say something. This may be the last time you get to talk to him." A giant lump sat in my throat as I tried to open my mouth and nothing came out. I didn't have the words. I wanted to say something *beautiful and meaningful* but came up short. My mind went blank and I felt so deeply sad. About 3o minutes passed and as I got up to leave, I kissed his head and was able to say, "*I love you*, Pup. Thank you for everything." It wasn't enough, but it was all I had in me. Since he passed, I have found the words and I have written them for him. It has been incredibly *healing* and writing it out made me feel like he was near again.

Write a letter to loved one that passed away.

Dear

_____

_____

_____

_____

Love,

IT'S ABOUT HAVING THE COURAGE TO
change the world
THE CHARISMA TO
CAPTIVATE PEOPLE'S MINDS,
THE STRENGTH TO
KEEP GOING
even when you fail.

{ }

We have all felt like we have been silenced at some point in our lives. We have all felt like no one was listening and that no one cared.

How did it make you feel?

The more I grow
the more I realize
so much can be
learned from
experiences and
sharing them with
others.

{ }

At my first job out of college, I worked for InventHelp. It was the most hilarious and important job I ever had. There, I learned that I need to speak out and speak up, that I should talk to the janitor the way I talk to the CEO of any company, to not let people intimidate you, to *laugh* when people are unnecessarily rude and that there are so many people out there that *believe* in themselves and trust their dreams and pursue them with this amazing *passion* that can't be stopped.

What was your first job?
What did you learn at that job that you still carry with you today?

You see, there is always going to be NEGATIVITY surrounding you, such is life. But there is infinitely more good in the world than bad, I TRULY BELIEVE THAT.

{ }

Describe 3 things that you can see right now that are beautiful.

{1} _____

{2} _____

{3} _____

LIKE MANY OTHER PEOPLE, I'VE SPENT
A LOT OF TIME
BEATING
MYSELF UP FOR WHAT
I HAVEN'T DONE YET.

{   }

Where do you see yourself in 5 years?

(There is no right or wrong answer.)

_____

_____

_____

_____

_____

_____

_____

_____

HUMAN BEINGS ARE

RESILIENT

{ }

After a speaking engagement at a middle school, a student reached out to me and told me that he was contemplating suicide. I couldn't believe it. My heart was breaking and pacing at the same time. Through a lot of emailing and a very long, tear-filled night, I was able to intervene and help this child get the help he needed. He was receptive. I was relieved and so grateful. The next day, he sent me a message telling me that he had been praying every night that God would send him a sign that he could get through his depression. He told me I was that sign. I will never forget that child or that moment. It was the kindest thing anyone has ever said to me.

What is the nicest compliment anyone has ever given you?

don't ever promote

H · A · T · E

it truly brings

=NOTHING=

to the

WORLD.

{ }

Do something nice for someone today.

Write out your experience here.

_____

_____

_____

_____

_____

_____

_____

Sooner or Later We All Do Really Dumb Stuff

{   }

When I wake up in the middle of the night, there are two memories that pop into my mind that make me want to rip my skin off. It never fails and I don't think I will ever forget what I said and how thoughtless and out of character it was for me. It may haunt me forever.

What is something you said to someone that you regret?
Are you ready to let that go and forgive yourself?

I WANT TO THANK MY

hilarious

AND UNBELIEVABLY
SUPPORTIVE FRIENDS WHO

believe

IN ME MORE THAN I
COULD EVER BELIEVE IN

myself.

{ }

When I think about my roommates in college, I think about how hard it had to be to live with a person with mental illness. Panic attacks, hospital visits and chaos surrounded my life and they had a front row seat for it all. But, I was *lucky* enough to live with people who were in my corner and had my back, *unconditionally*. They are some of the fiercest women to walk the earth and I *love* them for being so great during the darkest times in my life.

Who is the greatest friend(s) you ever had? Why are they so great?

(After you write it out. Take a photo of this page and text it to them if you can.)

I HAVE ALWAYS BEEN PROUD
TO BE MY DAD'S DAUGHTER
EVEN THOUGH WE HAVE
DEFINITELY HAD OUR
STRUGGLES. I HAVE
ALWAYS WANTED
HIM TO BE PROUD TO BE
MY DAD. BUT WHAT I
WITNESSED WHEN
HE DECIDED TO GIVE
UP DRINKING NOT ONLY
CHANGED HIS LIFE,
BUT SHAPED MINE.

{ }

That previous quote was written by me and is on ListenLucy.org.
My dad is my hero.

Who is the most influential person in your life? What did they do to impact your life?

_____

_____

_____

_____

_____

I guess my biggest fear in all of this is that I'll let this battle with myself and my fear of taking risks hold me back from experiencing all it is that I want to experience in life.

When I was in high school, I was an athlete. I had some issues with my hamstrings and had to wear these super thick compression shorts. During the game, the compression shorts made me sweat uncontrollably. The entire butt area of my shorts was soaking wet and the entire student section of the opposing team was chanting "Sweaty butt! Sweaty butt!" every single time I touched the ball. Talk about embarrassing.

What is the most embarrassing thing that has ever happened to you?

_____

_____

_____

_____

_____

He has taught me
to be comfortable with
WHO I AM
to learn
.. to make ..
GOOD DECISIONS,
to always be
able to
LAUGH AT MYSELF
and to
TRUST MY GUT. .

{ }

Our parents play a role in our lives-- whether they are the best or the worst, absent or overbearing, they are a part of us. Good, bad or ugly, these people gave you life.

Take this page and write a note to your parents telling them the most important things they taught you.

_____

_____

_____

_____

_____

_____

My Struggle,
my battle,
whatever you call it,
It isn't over yet
I know that. But I can see
Growth
and
Progress.
{ }

My mental illness is not an excuse to not accomplish. It is not an excuse to be rude. It is not an excuse for anything. I *accept* who I am and I work hard to *understand* myself, but I will never let my anxiety win. I will never give in.

What is the difference between giving in to your flaws and accepting your flaws? Why is it really important to NOT give in to your flaws?

_____

_____

_____

_____

_____

_____

Everyone
HAS A Story,
A Unique ONE
THAT MAKES THEM WHO
they are.

{ }

Look at yourself in the mirror.
Look into your eyes. It feels weird, right?
To stare at yourself?

What do you see? What
have you seen in your life
that has shaped you?

_____

_____

_____

_____

_____

_____

I HAVE LEARNED
THAT I AM
NO VICTIM
I AM A
SURVIVOR.

{ }

There have been times in my life that I just wanted to curl up in a ball and cry myself to sleep. My anxiety felt paralyzing and I was filled with a looming helpless feeling. If you have ever experienced that, write out how that felt. It's okay to remember. It helps you learn to cope.

Get the words out of your soul.

_____

_____

_____

_____

_____

_____

_____

you are
BEAUTIFUL.
you truly are.
EVEN WHEN YOU DON'T BELIEVE IT,
It's True

{ }

What is the most *beautiful* thing about you?
What do you *love* most about yourself?
Write it in the heart below.

HONESTLY, I'm · becoming · the PERSON that I always wanted TO BE.

{ }

Success means something different to everyone.
Define your terms of success.

_____

_____

_____

_____

_____

_____

_____

our
STRUGGLES
are the
building blocks
of our
STRENGTH.

{ }

How do you plan on being
the *light* in your own world?
What are you going to do to help
others *shine*?

If I can be true
to myself,
I can be true
to others.
As they say,
You can't
do it alone.

{ }

There are three things that my dad has said to me that I take with me every day.

{1.} Get in the right hand lane and *slow down*.
{2.} Humans beings are *resilient*.
{3.} It's nice to *be nice*. It's mean to be mean.

These things have been with me through many different times and have provided me with advice, wisdom and comfort.

What has someone said to you that you will never forget?

_____

_____

_____

_____

_____

STROKE
OF
LUCK
OR
THE
Universe's Plan?
WHO KNOWS?

{ }

Planning out your *life* and setting goals are two really important things. That being said, it is really hard to make a plan and stick to it because life is difficult and unexpected and unpredictable.

Write out your plans and talk about how you will learn to evolve and adapt as life happens.

you are a REAL LIFE SUPER HERO

You have written your heart out.
You are awesome.
Take this page to draw yourself
as a *superhero*.
You are ready to take on the world.

You made it this far on your journey...

NOW GET OUT THERE AND
KICK SOME ASS

{ }

{About Jordan}

Listen, Lucy is a place to express yourself freely, creatively and anonymously to find comfort in seeing you are not alone. Nationally recognized motivational speaker, mental health advocate and author, Jordan Corcoran (founder of Listen, Lucy) is a Mercyhurst College graduate with a story to share. During her freshman year, she was diagnosed with Generalized Anxiety Disorder and Panic Disorder. After going through a difficult struggle with coming to terms and learning to cope, Jordan created an outlet where people can openly and candidly share their own personal challenges and struggles.

Now Jordan's time is spent touring around the country speaking to college, high school and middle school students about her story and the importance of acceptance - of others and of yourself. She is the author of Listen Lucy Volume 1, has been featured on Today.com and UpWorthy for her self-love campaigns and was a keynote speaker at NAMI and other mental health organizations. This past year, she filmed The Acceptance Movement, a docu-series that showcases her speaking to 10 schools and organizations in the U.S. and revealing the powerful impact Listen, Lucy can have on an individual. Her mission is simple:

she wants to create a less judgmental and more accepting world.

CPSIA information can be obtained
at www.ICGtesting.com
Printed in the USA
BVOW07s2133081217
501982BV00003B/4/P